Short
Islamic Plays
for Children

Book 2

Short
Islamic Plays
for Children
2

Adapted by
Hassan Radwan

Illustrated by
M Ishaq

Short Islamic Plays for Children
Books 1 & 2

Adapted by Hassan Radwan
Illustrations by M Ishaq
Designed by Khaleel Muhammad
Edited by Tayyeb Shah

© 1999 Mountain of Light

This edition first published in 2000

Published jointly by Islamia Media (an imprint of Mountain of Light) and Ta-Ha

Mountain of Light Productions Ltd PO Box 7404 London N7 8JQ UK
Mountain of Light South Africa (PTY) LTD PO Box 43486 Industria 2042 South Africa
www.mountainoflight.com

Ta-Ha Publishers Ltd 1 Wynne Road London SW9 OBB UK
www.taha.co.uk

British Libary Cataloguing in Publication Data
A catalogue record of this book is available
from The British Library

Book 1
Mountain of Light ISBN 1 900675 39 0
Ta-Ha ISBN 1 84200 006 3

Book 2
Mountain of Light ISBN 1 900675 40 4
Ta-Ha ISBN 1 84200 011 X

Printed and bound by
De-Luxe Printers Park Royal London NW10 7NR UK
email : de-luxe@talk21.com

Contents

Introduction

This is a collection of short and mainly humorous plays that have been performed at Islamia Primary School in the London borough of Brent. They are a mixture of traditional and original tales that have been simplified and adapted for assemblies or as part of the school's annual Cultural Evening. Most of the plays would take no longer than 20 minutes to perform and have a simple moral or message and so would be appropriate for Eid assemblies or as part of a cultural presentation. I have included only the basic script and a nominal amount of directions and settings, as this will inevitably vary, depending on who and where they are to be performed and the intended audience. Of course, part of the fun for children in presenting plays is dressing up, and most of these plays provide great scope for the imagination. Some are set in the past at the height of the Islamic Caliphate, while others are contemporary. Please feel free to tailor them to your own needs. I hope also that they can be read and enjoyed, simply as they are, by anyone anywhere. I would like to thank the teachers and the children at Islamia Primary School for their valuable input

General Tips

I usually begin by reading the whole play to the children to make them familiar with the story. Then I choose the cast. Some of the plays require a large group of children while others have a small cast. I know from my own experience of working with a class of 30 children, all eager for a part, that it can be difficult to satisfy everyone. One way of including more children is to put "helpers" or "attendants", wherever possible! At other times it may be best to explain to some that they will get a chance in the next play! Whatever you choose to do, it is a good idea to have a "second" or "stand by" who must learn the lines and be ready to step in if someone drops out. Once the play is cast, give them copies of the script and let them read their own parts. This can be done sitting down in the classroom. Try to get them to enliven and animate their part with how they imagine the character might speak and move. I like to get them to act out the whole play "without scripts" as soon as possible, perhaps by the 3rd rehearsal. By doing this they have to think for themselves and learn their lines. They will also develop strategies to help one another out if they see someone is stuck. As a last resort you can prompt them yourself. It doesn't matter at all if they don't repeat their lines exactly as they are written, so long as what they say flows with the story. In fact, I encourage children to come up with their own improvements or ideas that will enhance the play and give them more confidence. But always make sure that the story itself is not strayed from. Some children seem to be natural actors, while others need plenty of support and direction.

The basic rules are, always face the audience, speak slowly and clearly and pause between each sentence or line. You can even get those children who are having difficulty with this, to actually count up to three to themselves, between each sentence. Only when they have learnt their lines well and are confident, will they really begin to "act" and "enliven" the play. When you reach this stage it is best not to change or introduce new material as it will often only throw and confuse them. Now it's just, practise makes perfect! (Well nearly! - but that's half the fun, isn't it?)

Hassan Radwan

(Adapted from 1001 nights)

The
Little Beggar

This story is about how the truth always comes out in the end no matter how hard you try to hide it and it shows how one lie leads to more lies.

One day Abu Ali & his wife are walking through the market when they see a little beggar by the side of the road

Little
Beggar   May Allah reward
          you a hundred
          times kind sir if you
          can spare one dirham
          for a hungry old man.

9

The Little Beggar

Wife	Oh Abu Ali, let us give this poor old man some money.
Abu Ali	We shall do better than that, my dear wife, we shall invite him home with us and let him share this fish we have brought today. (Turns to beggar) Come with us my friend so that we can share with you what Allah has given us.
Little Beggar	Oh thank you kind sir! Indeed Allah is generous to those who are generous to others.

They reach Abu Ali's house.

Abu Ali	Come in and sit down while my wife cooks the fish. Tell me old man about yourself.
Little Beggar	Oh sir, I am only a poor old man but I am happy with what Allah has given me. Indeed people call me the jolly beggar because I enjoy telling jokes and laughing so much.

The Little Beggar

Wife	Here you are, let us all enjoy this fish together!

They all start to eat.

Abu Ali	Tell us one of your jokes old man, to amuse us while we eat.
Little Beggar	Well sir, I remember I saw a wedding once when the bride could not stop hiccuping. Every time the Qadi asked her for her consent she replied by saying, "Hiccup".
Abu Ali & Wife	Ha ha ha, that is indeed very funny.
Little Beggar	Yes, the Qadi would say, "Do you give your consent to this marriage?" and she would say "Hiccup! Hiccup! Hiccup!"
Abu Ali & Wife	Ha ha ha!

The Little Beggar

Little Beggar	(Begins to choke on a fish bone) Hiccup! Hiccup! Hiccup!
Wife	Are you sure he is alright Abu Ali? Maybe he has swallowed a fish bone, he looks like he is choking!
Abu Ali	No! No! He is just making us laugh, he is a fine story teller. Ha ha ha ha!
Little Beggar	(Stretches his hands out for help) Hiccup! Hiccup! Hiccup!
Abu Ali	(Shakes his hands) Ha ha ha ha! Yes old man that is very funny!
Little Beggar	Hiccup! Hiccup! Hiccup! (Waves his arms about then falls to the floor).

The Little Beggar

Wife   Oh Allah forgive us, he was not joking, he was really choking and now he is dead!

Abu Ali   No! He is still playing a joke on us. Ha ha ha! Come on my friend, the joke is over! Now get up. (Abu Ali lifts his arm up but it flops back down) Oh no, you are right! He was not joking! It seems that he has choked to death on a fish bone! We have killed our guest.

The Little Beggar

Wife   The police will blame us and we will be executed for murder. What shall we do?

Abu Ali   Don't panic! We shall take his body out late at night when no one is looking and leave it on the steps of the doctor. He will think that he was sick and came for help but died on his doorstep.

They take his body out and leave it on the doctor's doorstep.

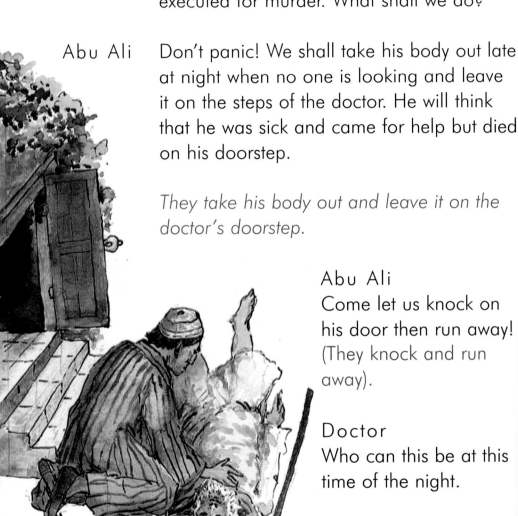

Abu Ali
Come let us knock on his door then run away! (They knock and run away).

Doctor
Who can this be at this time of the night.

Opens door and knocks body down the steps.

The Little Beggar

Doctor   Oh no! (Examines body) I have killed this poor man! He came to me for help and as he rested on my steps I kicked him down and killed him! Oh dear! What shall I do? I am supposed to be a doctor, I am supposed to save people's lives. Now I have killed this poor man, no one will ever trust me again and surely the police will arrest me and have me executed. I must get rid of his body before anyone sees. I know! I shall put him by the restaurant next door, perhaps the cook will think he ate too much and died by himself.

Doctor puts him by the restaurant.

Cook   I think I hear someone downstairs! I'd better go and see who is there.

Finds dead body.

The Little Beggar

Cook   What is this? A dead man by my door! Oh no, he must have eaten some of my food and it killed him. I knew that meat had gone off. Oh no what shall I do? I must quickly get rid of this body before I am arrested for murder. I shall lean him up in that dark street over there and people will think he just died by himself.

Leans him propped up by the wall and runs away. After a little while a merchant walks by.

Merchant   (Speaking to audience) What is that I see up ahead? It is a thief hiding in the dark shadows, waiting to jump out and rob me. But I shall teach him a lesson. Here is a big stick, I shall teach him not to steal from innocent people.

Walks by, then hits the body and it falls over.

The Little Beggar

Merchant	Oh dear! It seems that I do not know my own strength! I have hit him too hard and killed him. And who is that coming? It is the Chief of Police with the Qadi. What shall I do? They will arrest me for murder. I must hide quick. Ah! There is a box! I will hide in it.

Merchant hides his head in the box.

Qadi	What is this? A dead man. Who has done this terrible crime?

Chief of Police looks around and spots the merchant hiding in the box.

Chief of Police	Well my honourable Qadi, I think I have found the culprit. (Waves to the Qadi to come over and points to the box) Come on out young man you cannot hide from the justice of Allah.

The Little Beggar

Chief of Police arrests him.

Qadi   Do you admit that you
            killed this man.

Merchant   Allah sees and knows
            everything. Yes I
            killed him. May
            Allah forgive me.

Chie
of Police   Tomorrow you shall be executed in public
            for this crime.

Next day there is a big crowd.

Qadi   Oh servants of Allah. By his own
            admission this man has murdered this
            poor man whose body you see here. He
            shall be punished on this earth and may
            Allah take mercy upon him in the next life.
            Chief of Police carry out the sentence!

*Chief of Police raises his sword to cut off
his head.*

The Little Beggar

Cook   (Rushes forward) No! Stop! Stop! I cannot let you send an innocent man to his death. If I do I shall be forever damned. It was I who killed this poor man, may Allah forgive me! He ate some of my food that was bad and died at the door of my restaurant.

Qadi   What! Well it seems we have been saved from a great injustice. Take that man down oh Chief of Police and execute this man instead.

Chief of Police raises the sword to cut off his head.

Doctor   No! Stop! Stop! He is not the murderer, I am. He came to me for help and I kicked him down my steps and killed him!

Qadi   What! Can this be true! Well it seems that yet again we have been saved from a great injustice. Take that man down oh Chief of Police and execute this man instead.

The Little Beggar

Chief of Police raises the sword to cut off his head.

Abu Ali   No! Stop! Stop! The good doctor did not kill him, it was I. I invited this man home to eat and he choked to death on a fish bone. I am responsible for his death.

Qadi   Well bless my soul! What next! Is there anyone else in this crowd who claims to be responsible for this poor man's death?!

Abu Ali   No! Oh wise Qadi, I am the one responsible. No one else.

Qadi   Chief of Police! Take that man down and execute Abu Ali instead.

Doctor looks at dead man.

Doctor   No! Stop! Stop! Wait!

The Little Beggar

Qadi	Oh no! What is it now! Surely you are not going to say you killed him before he came to Abu Ali's house!
Doctor	This man is breathing!
Everyone	(Leaning forward) What?
Doctor	This man is still breathing listen!

Everyone puts their hands to their ears to listen and the man snores loudly!

Doctor	Abu Ali! Come here and help me sit him up! I shall try and remove the fish bone. *(Pats him on the back 3 times).*
Little Beggar	(Coughing) Where am I? What a funny dream I have had. I dreamt I was carried through the streets, thrown down stairs, dragged to a dark street and hit over the head!

The Little Beggar

Abu Ali	Praise be to Allah you are alive. I am so happy. Never again shall I lie or try to hide the truth.
Doctor, Cook & Merchant	And we too are sorry and will never try to hide the truth again.
Qadi	Let that be a lesson to you all. Allah sees and knows everything. Those who tell lies or do wrong can never escape punishment. They will always be found out. Either in this life or in the next life and the punishment of the next life is much worse.
Abu Ali	Come old man, let me take you home and give you some food.
Little Beggar	Er...that's very kind but no thanks. I don't feel hungry any more!

(Adapted from a traditional tale)

The Wise Qadi

The moral of this sketch is that you will be treated as you treat others

A poor man is passing by a restaurant where meat is being cooked.

Poor Man   Mmmmm! What a delicious smell is coming from that restaurant. How I wish I could eat some of the meat they are cooking, but I only have enough for a loaf of bread. I know, I will go and buy a loaf of bread and then eat it out here so that I can smell the meat as I eat the bread.

The Wise Qadi

So he gets the bread and sits outside eating and smelling the meat. Then he gets up to go.

Restaurant
   Owner   Stop! Wait! You can't just leave like that. You must pay me for all the smells you have enjoyed while eating your bread.

The Wise Qadi

Poor Man   But I can't pay you! I have no money.

Restaurant Owner   Then I shall take you to the Qadi.

They appear in front of the Qadi.

Restaurant Owner   Oh your honour, this man enjoyed a meal outside my restaurant and now refuses to pay me.

Qadi   What have you got to say for yourself.

Poor Man   It is true that I enjoyed the smell of the meat as I ate my bread, but I have no money to pay him.

Qadi   How much do you charge for the meat that he was smelling?

Restaurant Owner   50 pence

The Wise Qadi

Qadi   Look here, I have 50 pence. Now can
            you hear this?

            Drops the money on the table.

Restaurant
   Owner   Yes I can hear that.

Qadi   Right then! The sound of that money is
            the payment for the smell of your meat!
            Now go from here before I put you in
            jail for wasting my time!

(By Hassan Radwan)

Shayma Fasts Ramadan

This short sketch is aimed at encouraging understanding and toleration

The scene is a school playground in London where a group of children gather around.

Tom   Would you like some chocolate?

Friends   Oh yeah thanks.

Tom   What about you Aladdin?

They all laugh.

Shayma   Not for me thank you, I'm fasting!

Tom   What do you mean?

Shayma Fasts Ramadan

Shayma   I am a Muslim and Muslims fast
during Ramadan.

Tom   Do you mean you fast for a whole
month!

Mike   You must be starving!

They all laugh.

Shayma   We only fast during daylight hours but
we eat after the sun goes.

Shayma Fasts Ramadan

Martin   Go on have some chocolate, your mum and dad will never know.

Shayma   I don't fast because my mum and dad want me to fast. I fast for God.

Mike   Well God will never know!

Shayma   Of course God will know. He can see and hear everything.

Martin   My dad says that you Muslims are all weird and nutters.

Mike   Yeah it's true, you don't fit in here with us normal people.

Martin   You should go back to your own country.

Shayma   But this is my own country. I was born and brought up here just like you. The only difference between us is that I am a Muslim.

Shayma Fasts Ramadan

Mike	Yeah well, this is not a Muslim country so you should not be allowed to practise your religion.
Boy	So why don't you get on your magic carpet and fly away, Alladin?!

The children laugh and point and call names and push Shayma and taunt her with food. Chris and Gary then come running over.

Chris	Hey, you lot! Stop that, leave her alone!
Gary	Get away from her you bullies.
Chris	Its OK Shayma, don't take any notice of those children, they are just ignorant.
Gary	You know I am Jewish but I'm also British just like you are Muslim and British. This country has many different religions and we all belong here.

Shayma Fasts Ramadan

Chris   Yes and I am Christian and Christianity is one of the oldest religions in Britain but that doesn't give us the right to stop others from following their religion.

Gary   Don't feel embarrassed about fasting. I respect you for that. I respect anyone who follows their beliefs. You know we have a special time when we fast too, it is 10 days after Rosh Hashanah, the Jewish new year.

Chris   Yes and some Christians fast in Lent. Whatever your religion it doesn't matter, we should all be able to live together in peace.

Gary   Those children who make fun are the idiots, they are the sort that cause trouble between religions because they can't accept others for what they are. So don't take any notice of them.

Shayma Fasts Ramadan

Later in class.

Teacher I heard that there was a bit of trouble out in the playground.

Asiya Yes that's right Miss, Tom and his friends were bullying and making fun of Shayma, because she was fasting.

Teacher Is that right, Shayma? I shall put them in detention if they have been bullying you.

Shayma Oh Miss, it was nothing, I would rather forget it.

Later after school.

Gang walk by laughing and jeering.

Martin Oh look it's Alladin!

Mike Or is it Ali Baba?!

But then Tom walks over by himself.

Shayma Fasts Ramadan

Tom	Hey Shayma, I'm sorry for making fun of you! Don't take any notice of that lot, they just don't know any better.
Shayma	That's OK Tom, forget it.
Mike	Hey, what's got into Tom.
Martin	He must have gone soft, come on let's go.
	Gang walk off leaving Tom with Shayma.
Tom	You know Shayma, you are alright and I respect you for sticking to your beliefs. Martin's dad was wrong, you are not all weirdos.
Shayma	People are the same all over the world. There are good and bad people in every religion and race. We just want to practise our religion in peace.
Tom	Yeah, well that's OK by me!

33

(Adapted from a traditional tale)

Joha and the Donkey

The moral of this story is you can't please everyone.

Joha and his son are standing together with their donkey.

Joha   Today, I am going to market, to sell the donkey.

Son   Can I come Father?

Joha   Yes alright, go and fetch the donkey then.

Son   Yes Father.

Joha   I'll tell you what son, you sit up here on the donkey, while I walk. It is a long way to town and I don't want you to get tired.

Joha and the Donkey

Son   Anything you say Father.

They walk for a while then 2 passers-by see them.

1st Passer-by   Look at that, a strong, healthy young boy is sitting on the donkey.

2nd Passer-by   Yes and he is making his poor old father walk, how rude and bad-mannered children are today!

Joha   Oh dear! Maybe you shouldn't sit on the donkey son.

Son   Maybe you should sit on the donkey father.

Joha   Yes maybe I should.

They walk for a while then 2 passers-by see them.

3rd Passer-by   Look at that, a strong, healthy man is sitting on the donkey.

4th Passer-by   Yes and he is making his poor little son walk, how selfish and uncaring parents are today!

Joha and the Donkey

Joha   Oh dear! Maybe we should both walk son.

Son   Yes father.

They walk for a while then 2 passers-by see them.

5th
Passer-by   Look at those foolish people, both walking while they could be riding on the donkey!

37

Joha and the Donkey

6th Passer-by Yes, how ignorant and brainless people are today!

Son What shall we do now father?

Joha Oh dear! Maybe we should both sit on the donkey son.

Son Yes father.

They walk for a while then 2 passers-by see them.

7th Passer-by Look at that, a man and a boy both sitting on that poor donkey!

8th Passer-by Yes, they will break that poor creature's back, how cruel and inhuman people are today!

Son Now what shall we do father?

Joha Well, there is only one thing left, son! We will have to carry the donkey.

Joha and the Donkey

They walk for a while then 2 passers-by see them

9th Passer-by (Laughing) Ha ha ha, ho ho ho! Look at that! Those crazy people, they are walking to market carrying their donkey!

10th Passer-by (Laughing) Ha ha ha, ho ho ho! I think the donkey must have more brains than they have! How foolish and ignorant people are today.

Joha and the Donkey

Son   Oh dear, what are we going to do now father? It seems that no matter what we do people tell us we are doing the wrong thing.

Joha   That's right, whatever we do there is always someone who criticizes and disapproves of what we do. I think it is about time we stopped worrying about what other people think and do what we think is right.

Son   Yes father you are right, who cares what people think, so long as we know we are doing the right thing.

Joha   Come on son, get up on the donkey and let's go.

Son   Yes father.

(Adapted from 1001 Nights)

The Fisherman

The moral of this play is that good will always eventually triumph over evil.

NARRATOR

Once upon a time lived an old fisherman. He was poor but he was a very pious and good hearted man who gave all he had to others. One day he was fishing when he found a bottle. When he opened it, a genie came out.

The Fisherman

Genie   Choose how you wish to die!

Fisherman   But I set you free! Why do you repay me by killing me?

Genie   I have been trapped in that bottle for 300 years. For the first hundred years I promised to reward whoever set me free with gold. For the second hundred years I promised to reward whoever set me free with silver. But as the next hundred years passed I grew more angry and bitter and vowed to kill whoever set me free.

Fisherman   (Turns to audience) Oh dear, she is going to kill me. I must think of a way to trick her back into this bottle. (Turns back to Genie) Ha ha ha! You my dear friend are a liar! You are not a genie! You are only a poor fisherman like me. You have no powers. Did you really think that I would believe that you came out from this tiny bottle? Even the King of the Genies could not fit into this tiny bottle.

The Fisherman

Genie　It is true I tell you! I have been trapped in there for 300 years!

Fisherman　No you were hiding behind a rock and when you saw me open this bottle you thought you would trick me, by jumping out from behind the rock and pretending that you came out of the bottle. If it is really true then prove it to me.

Genie　Alright, then I will! Then you shall see that I am not a liar. I will show you that I am the most powerful genie that ever lived!

Genie returns to bottle.

Fisherman　(Quickly puts top back on) Ha ha! You may be the most powerful genie but you are also the most stupid. Now I shall throw you back into the sea where you came from!

The Fisherman

Genie   No! No! Stop! Please set me free! I promise I will not kill you.

Fisherman   What! Do you think that I am some sort of fool. You want me to let you out again so that you can kill me? Truly a Muslim should not get bitten twice!

Genie   Listen fisherman, a genie must never break its promise or it will lose its powers. Also, if you set me free I shall show you where there are the most marvellous fish. You have never seen such fish. They will make you rich.

Fisherman   (Turns to audience) Hmmmm? I wonder what I should do. Shall I open the bottle and let her out again? (Turns back to Genie in the bottle) You must promise that you will not harm me and if you do then you shall be cursed forever.

The Fisherman

Genie I promise I will not harm you and I shall show you the marvellous fish. I am bound by my promise.

Fisherman opens the bottle.

Genie Ha ha! I am free and although I wish only to kill you and feed your bones to the sharks I am bound by my promise and cannot harm you. Beyond that black mountain lies an enchanted lake that is full of the most wonderful fish. If you cast your net there you will find it so full you can hardly pull it up.

Fisherman I shall fish there if it pleases Allah.

Genie I will go now. But I warn you fisherman, if I ever lay eyes upon you again I shall make you into Shish Kebab and feed you to the vultures.

NARRATOR *The genie disappears. The next day the fisherman goes to the lake.*

The Fisherman

Fisherman   In the name of Allah I cast my net...
Allah is Great! What is this I see? My net
is full of fish! Each one a different colour
and shape. I have never seen such
marvellous fish as these.

Narrator   *The fisherman goes home to his wife.*

Fisherman   Oh Umm Salama, look at these fish,
they will indeed bring a good price at
the market.

**Umm
Salama**   Where did you get such fish?

The Fisherman

Fisherman From an enchanted lake. A genie told me where to find it.

Umm Salama I do not like the sound of that. Beware oh Abu Salama! These fish may be enchanted fish and will bring trouble to whoever eats them.

Fisherman What nonsense you are talking! Everything will be fine. I will take them to market immediately.

NARRATOR *The fisherman goes to market with his catch and sets up his stall. All the people stare in amazement and soon the Caliph hears about these marvellous fish.*

Fisherman Fresh fish! Come and get your fresh fish here! You have never seen such fish! Come and get your fish here!

Wazir Oh Commander of the Faithful, the people are all talking about some amazing fish that have been brought to market.

The Fisherman

Caliph   Let us go and see for ourselves.

Goes up to market stall.

Caliph   Truly I have never seen such fish! They will make a fine meal for tonight's banquet in honour of the Amir of Come-be Bolongo. Wazir you must buy all of them.

Wazir   Yes my Caliph! (Turns to fisherman) Fisherman! We shall give you 100 gold coins for these fish. Have them brought to the Caliph's kitchen this afternoon.

Fisherman   Yes sir!

In the Caliph's kitchens.

Cook   I have indeed never seen such fine fish, we shall prepare them with the very finest herbs and sauces so that the Caliph will be delighted.

The Fisherman

Amir   Ah! You honour me oh Caliph! I hope that our two countries will be able to agree a peace treaty so that our peoples can live in peace and happiness.

Caliph   Yes and I hope that you will see that our hospitality and generosity shows that we wish nothing but peace between our country and Come-Be Bolongo!

Cook   Dinner is served oh Commander of the Faithful.

Caliph
Then lay the food before our honoured guest

NARRATOR
They bring them on plates to the Caliph.

Amir
What marvellous fish!

49

The Fisherman

Caliph   Yes! This was prepared especially for you!

Amir   I shall now taste it.

Narrator   *But as the Amir puts his fork into the fish it jumps up, shouting!*

No more than 6 children arranged in pairs kneeling with heads bowed. Every time they speak they raise their heads then lower them.

Fish   Don't eat us! Don't eat us please! Don't eat us! Don't eat us please!

Amir   What is this? Are you playing a joke with me? How can a fish talk?

Caliph   Indeed, how can a fish talk? Especially ones that have been cooked and roasted!

Fish   Don't eat us! Don't eat us please! Don't eat us! Don't eat us please!

The Fisherman

One Fish	We were turned into fish by an evil genie!
Caliph	How can this be! Wazir! Send for the fisherman who sold us these fish.
NARRATOR	*The fisherman is brought before the Caliph.*
Caliph	These fish you sold us are still alive and what's more they can speak. Now tell me the truth! Are you some kind of evil magician, trying to poison me and my guests?
Fisherman	Oh no sir. I was sent to the lake beyond the black mountain by a genie, I did not know that the fish were enchanted.
Caliph	Take me there!
	They go to the lake.
Fisherman	This is the lake oh Caliph!

The Fisherman

NARRATOR *They hear the sound of crying.*

Wazir Listen! Over there I can hear crying.

NARRATOR *They enter a cave and see a young queen.*

Caliph Who are you and why are you crying?

Queen Oh Caliph! I have been stuck to this spot where you see me now for 300 years. I used to be queen of this land. One day I found out that my Wazir was plotting to kill me. He had planned the whole thing with an evil genie who was going to rule my kingdom. When I found out he tried to escape on a horse, but fell and fatally injured himself. When the evil genie heard about this she tried to make him better but was only able to keep his body alive. He cannot move or speak and lies on the other side of the lake. Then in her rage she destroyed our city and turned it into a huge lake and all the people into fish. She put a spell on me that has kept me fixed to the floor of this cave.

The Fisherman

Caliph   This is terrible, but can't anyone break her spell?

Queen   Only the evil genie can break the spell herself but she was imprisoned by the King of the Genies 300 years ago and can never escape. I and my people are doomed forever.

Caliph   This must be the same genie that the fisherman found. I believe Allah has brought me hear to here your sad story, for a reason. Indeed I must help you.

Wazir   But how shall we help her and what shall we do?

Caliph   I have a plan. You must go to where the body of the evil wazir lies and carry him away to my prison. I shall take his place. You can leave the rest to me.

The Fisherman

NARRATOR   *They remove the evil wazir and carry him away to prison. The Caliph takes his place - all wrapped up.*

Genie goes to the Queen.

Genie   Ha ha! I am free at last and when my Wazir is better again we shall rule your kingdom and watch you suffer for eternity.

Queen   May Allah punish you for your evil.

Genie   Ha! No one can stop me. You are responsible for what happened to my Wazir. You shall suffer for the rest of your life for that. Now I shall go to him and see if he has recovered yet. Soon he will get better and then I shall kill you! Ha ha ha ha!

NARRATOR   *The Genie goes to what she thinks is the evil wazir's body, but is really the Caliph in disguise.*

The Fisherman

Genie   I have returned, are you better now? Have the years cured you yet? Please speak to me! At least one word!

Caliph   How can I be better when I can never sleep for the cries and groans of the Queen.

Genie   What joy to hear you speak! What do you wish me to do?

Caliph   Set the Queen free so that I do not hear her cries! Hurry! I cannot stand it any longer.

Narrator   *The genie goes back to the Queen.*

Genie   My Wazir has commanded me to free you and I do this only so he gets better.

Genie raises her arms and makes a spell.

Queen   I am free at last! I am free!

The Fisherman

Genie   Now go away from this place and never come back or I will kill you.

Narrator   *The Genie returns to the Wazir.*

Genie   I have returned, are you better now?

Caliph   What you have done is not enough to cure me. Every day at midnight all the people whom you changed into fish lift their heads out of the lake and cry out for help. Go quickly and break the spell upon them so I can have peace.

The Genie goes to the fish.

Fish   Help us! Help us!

Genie   My Wazir has commanded me to free you and I do this only so he gets better.

Fish   We are free at last! We are free!

The Fisherman

Genie   Now go away from this place and never come back or I will kill you all.

NARRATOR   *The Genie returns to the Wazir.*

Genie   Are you quite well now?

Caliph   Come near, I cannot hear you.

Genie   Are you quite well now?

Caliph   Come nearer, I still cannot hear you.

Genie   Are you quite well now?

NARRATOR   *She comes nearer and the Caliph jumps up and kills her with his sword.*

Genie   (Dying words) Ah! I have been tricked!

The others come out of hiding.

Caliph   Rejoice for your enemy is dead.

Queen   Thank you oh Caliph, for ridding us of this evil curse.

57

The Fisherman

Caliph   Do not thank me but thank Allah who knows and sees all things. He has power over all things and He is the Merciful, the Wise!

**Queen &
her subjects**   Allahu Akbar! Allahu Akbar!

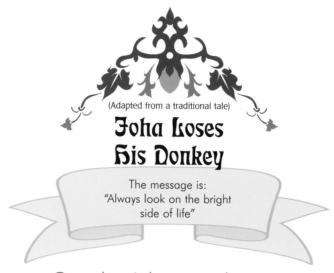

(Adapted from a traditional tale)

Joha Loses His Donkey

The message is:
"Always look on the bright side of life"

One day Joha came home.

Wife   Assalamu-Alaykum Joha.

Joha   Assalamu-Alaykum.

Wife   Supper is nearly ready, but first go and put the donkey in the stables and then wash your hands.

Joha   Donkey? Did I take the donkey out with me this morning?

Wife   Of course you did!

Joha   Oh dear, well it is not with me now. I must have lost it on my way home.

Wife   Oh Joha! Come on let's see if we can find it.

They both search.

Joha   "Oh I'm so glad! Oh I'm so glad!" (4 times).

Wife   Oh Joha, why do you keep saying, "Oh I'm so glad! Oh I'm so glad?" Surely you cannot be so glad that you have lost your donkey?

Joha   Oh I am so glad because when my donkey was lost, I was not riding it, or I would be lost too!

(Adapted from a story
by Nurain Jamal -
aged 9)

Silly Sammi & Foolish Farouk

The moral of this play is that there is more than one way of sharing something

Silly Sami	Oh Yummie! I have a tasty bar of chocolate.
Foolish Farouk	Can I have some?
Silly Sami	No, get lost!
	They fight.
Cousin Kauthar	No! Stop! You shouldn't fight. You must share it instead.
Silly Sami & Foolish Farouk	Share it? How do we do that?

Cousin Kauthar	All you have to do is cut it in half.
Silly Sami & Foolish Farouk	Oh! That's a good idea! Cut it in half!
	They cut it in half and share it!
Silly Sami	I'm feeling sleepy. I'm going to sleep on this bed.
Foolish Farouk	I'm sleepy also and I want to sleep on this bed.

Silly Sami & Foolish Farouk

They fight.

Silly Sami No stop, remember what cousin Kauthar said. We must share it.

Foolish Farouk How do we do that?

Silly Sami You remember, we have to cut it in half.

Foolish Farouk OK, here's a big saw.

They start to cut the bed.

Cousin Kauthar What are you doing?

63

Silly Sami & Foolish Farouk

Silly Sami & Foolish Farouk	We are sharing the bed.
Cousin Kauthar	You don't share like that. You have to sleep on it together. One of you can sleep on the top and the other can sleep on the bottom.
	They go to sleep and snore. They wake up.
Silly Sami	Time to get up. I will put these trousers on.
Foolish Farouk	But I want to put those ones on too!
	They fight.
Silly Sami	No stop, remember what cousin Kauthar said. We must share them.
Foolish Farouk	How do we do that?

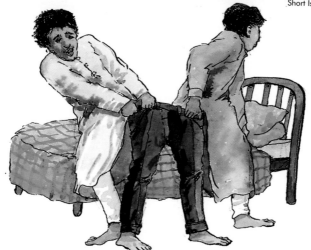

Silly Sami	You remember she said we have to sleep on the bed together so that means we have to put these trousers on together.
Foolish Farouk	OK! You put one leg on you and I'll put one leg on me.
	They walk around like that.
Cousin Kauthar	What are you doing?
Silly Sami & Foolish Farouk	We are sharing the trousers.
Cousin Kauthar	You don't share like that. You have to wear it one day and the other one wears it the next day.

Silly Sami & Foolish Farouk

Silly Sami & Foolish Farouk	Oh! We understand now.
	One of them puts it on. They go out.
Silly Sami	Oh that was a good day out.
Foolish Farouk	Yes! But now it is dark we must light our candles.
Silly Sami	Oh dear. There is only ONE match left.
Foolish Farouk	That's OK, we can SHARE it! Remember what cousin Kauthar said, you can use it first and then you can give it to me to use.
Silly Sami	Yes of course.
	Silly Sami uses it then BLOWS IT OUT & gives it to Foolish Farouk who tries his best to light it.
Cousin Kauthar	What are you doing?

Silly Sami & Foolish Farouk

Silly Sami & Foolish Farouk	We are SHARING the match.
Cousin Kauthar	You can't use a match 2 times. You have to light both candles while the match is still lit.
Silly Sami & Foolish Farouk	Oh! We understand now!
Cousin Kauthar	Never mind, look I have a lovely surprise for you. Some ice cream and this time you don't have to share it because there are TWO!
Silly Sami & Foolish Farouk	Now that's what I call a LOVELY surprise!

OPINIONS REGARDING THE USE OF IMAGES AND ILLUSTRATIONS FOR CHILDREN

`Aa'ishah said, "I used to play with dolls in the presence of the Prophet ﷺ, and my girlfriends used to play with me. Whenever Allah's Messenger ﷺ would enter, they would hide from him. So he called them to play with me."

SAHIH AL BUKHARI, VOL 8, P.95, NO.151 AND SAHIH MUSLIM, VOL.4, P. 1299, NO. 5981.[1]

In the classic commentary on Sahih Al Bukhari, entitled Fat-h al-Baaree, Ibn Haajar al-`Asqalaanee wrote the following:

'This hadeeth is used as evidence for the permissibility of making dolls and toys with human and animal forms for the purpose of girls playing with them. This category has been specifically excluded from the general prohibition against making images. `Iyaad stated this to be categorically so and related that it was the position of the majority of scholars. He further related that they permitted the selling of toys for girls in order to train them for their youth in their household affairs and in dealing with their children.[2]

Ibn Hibbaan entitled a chapter in his saheeh, "The permissibility for children and women to play with Toys" and another, "A man's giving permission to His Wife to Play with Dolls", however, his not limiting the permission to child wives, is a questionable position.[3]

Aboo Dawood and an-Nasaa'ee collected this hadeeth in another chain from 'Aa' ishah in which she said, "When Allah's messenger ﷺ arrived after expedition to Tabuk or Khaybar, the wind raised an end of a curtain which hung in front of my closet, revealing some dolls which belonged to me. He asked me, 'What is this?' I replied; 'My dolls.' He saw among them a horse made of cloth with wings, and asked, 'What is this I am seeing among them?' I replied; 'Have you not heard that Solomon had horses with wings?' Allah's Messenger ﷺ laughed so heartily that I could see his molar teeth." This hadeeth is very clear that the meaning of playthings (lu'ab) mentioned in the earlier narration does not refer to humans.

Al-Khattaabee stated that this hadeeth indicates that playing with dolls is not like playing with other images which were warned about. And permission was given to 'Aa'ishah regarding them because she was not mature at the time. [Al-Khattaabee's] categorical statement [that 'Aa"ishah was not mature at the time] is questionable, however, it is a possibility. 'Aa'ishah was close to fourteen or past fourteen at the time of the Battle of Khaybar. As regards at the time of the Battle of Tabuk, she had definitely reached maturity by then. Thus the narrations of this hadeeth which mentioned Khaybar are more likely correct and they agree with Khattaabee's opinion, which is more preferable than the contradictions [inherent in those which mention Tabuk]'.[4]

Ar-Rubayya` bint Mu`awwath related that the Prophet ﷺ sent a messenger to the village of Ansaar on the morning of the day of `Aashooraa (10th Muharram) to announce that whoever had already eaten should not eat any more and fast the rest of the day; and whoever was already fasting should complete the fast. She went on to say, "Since then, we used to fast on that day and also make the boys fast. We would make toys out of wool for them, and if any of them cried for food, he would be given one until it was time to break the fast."[5]

The Islamic magazine, al-Usrah, published in Saudi Arabia grappled with the issue of figurative illustrations when they decided to launch a magazine especially targeted towards children. They wanted to provide an alternative to what was present in the marketplace, which had little Islamic contents and was introducing some unislamic values to their readers. They noticed that every single magazine for children printed in the Arab world as well as in the west was filled with illustrations of children, animals, etc. The reality is that colourful drawings are something that children are attracted to. If given the choice between reading a text with pictures and a text without them, they will always choose the illustrated text. The editors of al- Usrah thought of trying to address this situation by using drawings of inanimate objects with features added to make them look like live characters, but they decided that technique was too limited to use for the whole magazine.

In researching the Sharee'ah issues related to the drawings of living creatures, they reached the following conclusions:

1. The basic rule regarding figurative illustrations is that they are haraam.

2. The reason for the prohibition is that it involves imitations of Allah's attributes of Creator and Bestower of Forms, in addition to the role of images in paving the way for shirk by magnifying the greatness of the illustrated beings, which leads to their being worshipped.

3. There is an exception to the general prohibition for children's toys, as is specifically indicated in hadeeth texts, due to the fact that the main reason for the prohibition is not present and that there is a tangible benefit in their use.

4. This exception to the prohibition of image-making is also applicable to whatever represents a tangible benefit, given consideration by the Shee'rah, or prevents or removes an expected harm, whether in the fields of education, public safety or other areas.

5. Pictures drawn specially for children enter into the exception, by analogy with children's dolls and toys, on the one hand, and in order to realise the benefits recognised by the Sharee'ah and due to the pressing need for them in contemporary children's stories, on

the other.

In this regard Shaykh Naasiruddeen al-Albaanee stated in his book, Addab az-Zafaaf, "These two hadeeths (the hadeeth of `Aa'ishah's dolls and the hadeeth about the Sahaabah's practice of giving their fasting children toy figures to distract them from their hunger) indicate the permissibility of creating images and owning them when their is an educational benefit in doing so, one that will help in the cultivation and development of the person-ality. Whatever else is of benefit to the Muslims and Islam may be included in the same ruling of permissibility of picture making and use, but everything beside that remains under the basic prohibition." [p.196]

In the same vein, Shaykh `Abdullah ibn Jibreen responded to a long, detailed question on image-making put to him by the editors of *al-Usrah* magazine by saying, "I have considered what has been mentioned in the question con-cerning the temptations and deviations to which the Muslim youths are being exposed both within and without the lands of the Muslims in the form of films and magazines, which are (so widespread as to be virtually) unavoidable, which have filled the Muslims' houses and palaces, and which cause Muslim children to imitate what they see and hear and read in them in their speech and actions, the contents of which are frequently evil and corrupt. [After weighing these factors,] I say:

When an alternative exists to engage children and youth which is free, or relatively free, from such corrupt ideas and values, I see it as permissible, because among the basic principles of the Shee'rah is choosing the lesser of two evils in order to avoid the greater harm. Without any doubt, for Muslim children to be busy in reading Islamic magazines that include some pictures used to make the ideas clearer is less serious than their habitual viewing of movies and picture (magazines) that ruin their morals, pervert their innocence and divert them away from good. That is what is apparent to me, and Allah knows best."

Shaykh`Abdul `Aziz al-Qaari' (Imam of Masjid Qubaa' and professor of Tafseer and Qur'anic recitation at the Islamic University of Madeenah) had this to say about image-making:
"Regarding the Hadeeth of Aa'ishah that she played with dolls in the presence of the Prophet ﷺ, and, in some versions of the hadeeth, that one of the dolls was in the shape of a winged horse, and that when the Prophet ﷺ asked her about it, she replied, 'Didn't you hear that (Prophet) Suliman had a horse with wings?' to which the Prophet ﷺ responded by laughing; this hadeeth indicates the permissibility of children's figurative toys, owning them and using them, whether they are clearly representative or not, and whether skillfully or crudely fashioned. There is no basis in the hadeeth for making a distinction. Those who say that Aa'ishah's dolls were not distinctly repre-

sentative have made an arbitrary judgment not based on any evidence.

What do you say about a winged horse?

The variation in the texts on this subject, from severe threats of punishment to less severe threats and from the prohibition of the use (of wings) to allowing their use, indicates that the law revolves around the consideration of the accompanying benefit and harm. If the law was fixed on prohibition, far be it for the Prophet 鷺 to allow Aa'ishah to play with those dolls and that horse, all of which were three-dimensional images. From that we know that the rule is connected to benefit and harm. If the harm involved is dominant, as in the case of pictures idols and statues worshipped in place of Allah, or in the case of pictures of important or pious people hung on walls as a sign of respect, which is a major avenue leading to shirk, the rule is prohibited. On the other hand, if the benefit is clearly dominant, as in the case of children's toys, or images on rugs or pillows, etc., which are put to use without respect, then the rule is permissibility. Children's magazines, books and stories take the same ruling as children toys and dolls, since the benefit in toys and dolls is no clearer than that in these other (educational) media. This matter is not restricted to children either. Even for adults, it is permissible for them to employ images in all their educational and information media, as long as the benefit from such use is dominant over the harm."

Complied by **Dr Abu Ameenah Bilal Phillips**

Notes

1 See also Sunnan Abu Dawud, vol, p.1373, no. 4913.
2 Ibn Hajar stated here that some scholars like Ibn Battaal, held that the hadeeth of Aa'ishah was abrogated and that Ibn Abee Zayd related trhat Maalik disliked that a man purchase dolls for his daughter. Consequently. ad-Daawoodee also concluded that the *hadeeth* was most likely abrogated. Fat-h al-Baaree, vol. 10, p. 544.
3 Ibn Hajar added here that al-Bayhaqee, after narrating this hadeeth stated that the prohibition against making images is undeniable / unshakeable, therefore this permission to 'Aa'ishah should be considered as having taken place before the prohibition. Ibn al-Jawzee catergorically held that this was the correct position. Al-Munthiree stated that if the toys were image-like, the permission to 'Aa'ishah must have been before the prohibition. Otherwise, playthings without images may also be called toys/dolls. Al-Haleemee stated catergorically that if the toy has an image like an idol, it is not permissible, otherwise it is permissible. After quoting ad-Daawoodee as saying *thatal-la'ib bi al-banaat* meant playing with "young girls" and that *bi* here meant *ma'a* (along with), Ibn at-Teen thoroughly refuted him. [Ibn Hajar went on to say that] the narration of Ibn 'Uyaynah related in al-jaami' from Hishaam ibn 'Urwah "... and some young girls used to come and play with them along with me," and that of Jareer from Hishaam "I used to play with dolls (al-banaat), and they were toys," collected by Aboo 'Awaanah aand others also refutes ad-daawoodee. Fat-h al-Baaree, vol. 10, p.544. Sunan Abu Dawud, vol. 3, 1373, no. 4914 and authenticated in the Saheeh Sunan Abee Daawood, vol. 3, p.932, no.4123
4 Fat-h al-Baaree, vol.10, pp. 543-4
5 Sahih Al Bukhari, vol. 3 pp. 103-4, no.181

GLOSSARY

Caliph	Muslim Ruler. Also called 'Commander of the Faithful'.
Grand Wazir / Wazir	Chief Minister.
Baghdad	A major city in the Middle East.
Qadi	Judge.
Insha-Allah	God-willing.
Khatam	A ring bearing the royal seal.
Dunya	This world.
Du'a	Making supplication to Allah.
Assalamu-Alaykum	Islamic greeting meaning 'Peace be upon you'.
Walaykum-Assalam	Reply to Islamic greeting meaning 'And unto you be peace'.
Allahu-Akbar	God is Great

A *is for* ALLAH

It took 20 years for Yusuf Islam to develop *A is for Allah* from a song to a monumental and attractive work. The book comprises of 68 beautiful full colour pages and over 40 photographs describing, for children and adults, the essence of Islam through the Arabic alphabet. The album on Double CD and Double Cassette complements the Book and includes:

Hardback Book · Double CD · Double Cassette
Cover Poster · A is for Allah Song Lyrics Poster
2 CD + Book & postcard pack
2 Cassette + Book & postcard pack

Audio version includes:

· COMPLETE BOOK NARRATED BY **YUSUF ISLAM**

· QUR'ANIC RECITATION BY RENOWNED EGYPTIAN QARI **SHEIKH MUHAMMAD GIBREEL**

· ENGLISH TRANSLATION READ BY IMAM HAMZA YUSUF FROM THE USA

· 8 SONGS - 7 ARRANGED & WRITTEN BY **YUSUF ISLAM** INCLUDING THE TITLE TRACK A IS FOR ALLAH - AND INTRODUCING ZAIN BHIKHA FROM SOUTH AFRICA

· GUEST APPEARANCE BY MALAYSIA'S WORLD FAMOUS NASHEED GROUP RAIHAN PERFORMING HARMONIES ON YUSUF'S SEAL OF THE PROPHETS

· ADHAN BY **MUAZZIN OF MAKKAH**

· APPROX. RUNNING TIME 101 MINUTES

POSTERS
594mm x 420mm

The Life of the Last Prophet ﷺ

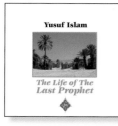

Yusuf Islam

With over 300,000 copies sold since 1995, this spoken-word recording of the life of Prophet Muhammad ﷺ was the first official release by Yusuf Islam since his departure from the music business as Cat Stevens back in 1978. The biography is fully authenticated and approved by an international group of 'ulema (scholars) and contains selected verses of the Qur'an, recited by the respected Egyptian Qari' (reciter) Sheikh Muhammad Al-Minyaoui. It also includes the song Tala'a al-Badru 'Alayna, and a beautiful rendition of the adhan (call to prayer) and is the best concise biography on the Prophet Muhammad ﷺ available in English.

Approx. running time: 60 minutes

CD £9.99 Cassette £4.99 Hardback Book
Giftcase - Hardback Book + CD
Giftcase - Hardback Book + Cassette

Prayers of the Last Prophet ﷺ

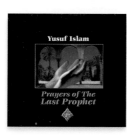

Yusuf Islam

Prayers of The Last Prophet ﷺ contains a collection of du'as (supplications) as used by the Prophet Muhammad ﷺ. Narrated by Yusuf Islam and structured around phases of the day, these du'as cover a range of everyday activities seeking God's guidance. All are derived from Qur'an and Hadith and are fully authenticated. Prayers also contains Qur'anic recitation by the acclaimed Egyptian Qari' (reciter) the late Sheikh Mahmoud Khalil Alhousari and features 3 new songs including Yusuf Islam's If You Ask Me.

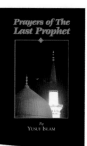

Approx. running time: 60 minutes

CD Cassette Hardback Book
Giftcase - Hardback Book + CD
Giftcase - Hardback Book + Cassette

WELCOME
TO THE QUR'AN
Gateway to Faith
Yusuf Islam

Welcome to the Qur'an: Gateway to Faith is the first in the Islamic Circle Talks series, adapted from talks given by Yusuf Islam at Regent's Park Mosque, London. In this talk, Yusuf, who embraced Islam after having read the Qur'an in 1977, takes the listener on a journey of discovery as he introduces the majestic beauty of the Qur'an through the gateway of faith. Includes Qur'anic recitation by Egyptian *Qari* Ahmed Ali Abd al-Tawab and nasheed *Qur'anu Rabbee*.

Approx. running time:
48 minutes

Cassette

THE ISLAMIC CIRCLE TALKS SERIES

The Prophetic Art of
COMMUNICATION
Introduction to Da'wah
Yusuf Islam

Tape 2 in the Islamic Circle Talk series is Yusuf Islam talking about how the Prophets throughout time delivered God's message. This talk reminds us all of the importance of inviting people to Islam and particularly the methodology to use following the *sunnah* (example) of the last Prophet Muhammadﷺ

Approx. running time:
38 minutes

Cassette

GUIDE TO THE MOSQUE
Abdullah Ibrahim

Ideal for children and beginners to Islam!

Leading Muslims of
the Past
and Present

MUSLIM LEGENDS

An educational audio-tour of London's Central Mosque and Islamic Cultural Centre. Recorded in 1982 by the late Abdullah Ibrahim, this release is accompanied with English translation of the Qur'an read by Yusuf Islam. With a richly enjoyed style of narration, Abdullah Ibrahim emphasises the central importance of the Mosque in the life of a Muslim.

Approx. running time: 55 minutes

Cassette

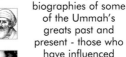

Short but concise forty minute biographies of some of the Ummah's greats past and present - those who have influenced millions of Muslims and non-Muslims all over the world and throughout the ages.

Running time: 40 minutes

Cassette

A SIMPLE GUIDE TO PRAYER
for beginners

BOOK

"I HAVE NOT CREATED JINN AND MANKIND FOR ANY OTHER PURPOSE EXCEPT TO WORSHIP ME..."
Holy Qur'an 51:56

This paperback book and tape provide a basic introduction to salah (prayer) to both newcomers to Islam and those wishing refresh their basic knowledge of prayer.

Approx. running time: 60 minutes

Book

Cassette

CASSETTE

In partnership with
THE ISLAMIC FOUNDATION

30th Juz *of the* Holy Qur'an

Arabic recitation by Sheikh Muhammad Al-Minyaoui

English narrated by Yusuf Islam

With Islam today having over one billion followers, the Qur'an is probably the most widely read book in the world, with sections of it being recited at least five times a day by Muslims during their daily prayers.

This recording features the original Arabic recited by the respected Egyptian *Qari* Sheikh Muhammad Al-Minyaoui with each verse being followed by its English translation read by Yusuf Islam. The Arabic recitation style is *tartil* and the English narration is based upon *The Noble Qur'an* translated by Dr. Muhammad Taqi-ud-Din Al-Hilali and Dr. Muhammad Muhsin Khan.

Approx. running time 120 minutes

Double Cassette

Double CD

 In partnership with Darussalam

'Qur'anic Alphabet'

Yusuf Islam

Using Qur'anic verses and pictures, *'Qur'anic Alphabet'* takes us through the 28 letters of the arabic alphabet. 63 pages

Hardback Book
Paperback Book

Islamic Teachings Course

Volumes 1, 2 & 3

Presented by the well respected scholar Jamal Badawi, *Islamic Teachings Course* Volumes 1,2 & 3, answers hundreds of questions on Islam in a simple paper-back format.

Vol. 2 124pp
Vol. 2 80pp
Vol. 3 133pp

THE SYLLABUSES
Islamia Primary School

The Syllabuses contain all National Curriculum subjects together with Arabic, Qur'an and Islamic studies. They are presented in a durable A4 size ring binder with colour dividers and is designed to be updated. It is ideal for anyone involved in primary school education as well as parents.
12 subjects, 218pp
(Individual subjects also available)

OFFICIAL UK VERSION

RAIHAN

Raihan are the best nasheed (song) group in the world! Having taken Malaysia by storm, they have quickly gone on to achieve international acclaim. Singing in Malay, Arabic and English, and with songs full of fantastic harmonies, they have redefined Islamic nasheeds. Jamal Records is proud to present the official UK versions of *Puji Pujian* and *Syukur* which come complete with English sleeve notes and lyrics.

PUJI PUJIAN

Their premier album made them big, selling over 650,000 copies and features the hit tracks *Rakan Selawat (Maulid)* and *Assolatuwasalam*.

CD

Cassette

SYUKUR

Syukur, their second album, contains 2 songs by Yusuf Islam including the exquisite *God is the Light*.

CD

Cassette

In partnership with **wea** ZAMRUD

Khaleel Muhammad

Ever wanted something for the kids that was hip, entertaining AND with Islamic morals??? Well, have no fear Hakim our intrepid 13-year-old Muslim hero is here!

the adventures of
HAKIM

Written and read by Khaleel Muhammad, *The Adventures of Hakim* is a great audio-book for the young and the young at heart and includes the catchy song *'Streetwise Believer'*.

Approx. running time: 61 minutes

Double Cassette music
Double Cassette non-music

A rich and fascinating collection of stories of faith, courage and heroism
sensitively written for children by the author of the best-selling
The Muslim Women's Handbook.
This Book includes full colour illustrations.

44pp Paperback A4   ISBN 1 897940 34 3

£ 4.95